D1486414

Edition Eulenburg

THE HIGH MASS
DIE HOHE MESSE

B minor

by

JOHANN SEBASTIAN BACH

*

Edited from the score of the Bach-Gesellschaft
and with Foreword by

FRITZ VOLBACH

Ernst Eulenburg, Ltd, London, W. 1
Edition Eulenburg, G.m.b.H., Zürich
Ernst Eulenburg & Co., G.m.b.H., Mainz
Edition Eulenburg, Inc, New York

JOHANN SEB. BACH, MASS IN B MINOR

The Bach B minor Mass soars above like some huge, primitive mountain rock. Its summit is lost in the clouds, in an infinity of sunlit blue; lonely und sublime, it is unapproachable by any other music.

The art of Bach is an art which yearns towards the eternal; through love and the grace of God it finds the way; love which entwines the transient with the everlasting, the finite with the infinite. A yearning towards the unknown, to all that is undisclosed, a yearning, "only to be stilled by yearning."

Precise information as to the origin of the work cannot be given. The first two sections of the Mass, the *Kyrie* and *Gloria* were added by Bach after a petition to the King of Saxony for the title of Court composer, bearing the date July 27th 1733. Spitta places the composition of the remaining sections — *Credo, Sanctus* and *Hosanna* — between 1734 and 1738. The *Agnus Dei* goes back to an aria in the Cantata "Lobet Gott in seinen Reichen," whilst the *Dona nobis pacem* is, musically, a repetition of the *Gratias agimus* which also originates from a Cantata entitled "Wir danken dir."*)

That a protestant like Bach composed Masses need not astonish us. Luther had not abolished the Mass, but merely taken from it the character of sacrifice by the rejection of the sacrificial act; the established parts — the *Ordinarium missae* — remain in evangelical worship. Hence, from after the Reformation down to the time of Bach, a succession of evangelical masters composed masses for the service of God. The wonderful poetry was reserved for them, poetry which explores all the heights and depths of religious feeling, connecting and comparing images, stronger, more moving and majestic than ever before or since. But who more fitted to depict the glory of this vast kingdom of Heaven, to tread this secret land of yearning, lying far behind the world of reality, than J. S. Bach, the greatest German mystic?

The first section of the work is born of deep longing. The *Kyrie eleison* reveals a yearning for delivrance from this world of grief, and the desire to ascend into the grace of God. The whole impressive picture is portrayed in the form of a five-part fugue, the Chorus being divided into 2 Soprani, Alto, Tenor and Bass. Besides the quintet of strings the orchestra is composed of 2 Flutes, 2 Oboe d'amore (namely Oboes a third lower than the ordinary instrument, and softer in tone) and Bassoons. The lowest voice, the Continuo is confided to the Cellos, Double basses and Organ. *The latter instrument completes the harmony through figured bass***). This not only

---

*) For the relationship between the *Qui tollis* and the Cantata "Schauet doch und sehet", between the *Patrem omnipotentem* and "Gott wie ist dein Name", between the *Crucifixus* and "Weinen, Klagen", the *Hosanna* and "Preise dein Glücke", see A. Schweitzer: J. S. Bach (1908), page 684 etc.

**) Compare the Introduction to Händel's "Messiah" for further information about the Continuo and its treatment.

II

applies to this movement, but also to all the others of the Mass. In spite of the massive proportions of the Kyrie, its structure is clear and distinct. Five powerful opening bars are followed by the evolution of the orchestral fugal theme, to be then taken up by the Chorus in solid, broad exposition. But its contents are not yet exhausted, for there follows a second climatic development in the shape of an orchestral interlude similar to the first part.

The *Christe eleison* which follows is set as a duet. It is left to the organ *alone* to fill in the harmony. The atmosphere is that of hope and confidence. This mood is also maintained in the second *Kyrie*, a piece of great beauty and clarity in the vocal handling. With the exception of the powerful basic support, the instruments follow the voices, and the wonderful final working-up in the last nine bars, so rich in modulation, should be specially noted.

The second portion of the work, the *Gloria,* is not set in one continuous spell, as was customary with the earlier masters (and also with Beethoven), but is split up into several portions, the first three of which form one complete group. The opening Chorus, with its triumphant trumpet calls, is of great force and brilliance. Its division follows the nature of the text. In the *Laudamus,* solo voice and solo violin vie with one another in praise of the Lord. The *Gratias agimus* is founded upon two themes, the main theme at the very start, and the subsidiary theme combined with it on the words "propter magnam gloriam tuam."

With the following *Domine Deus* there begins a song of praise to Jesus Christ. Solo passages and Chorus are again interchanged. The *Qui tollis* is for me worthy of special remark. Here, of the wood-wind instruments, the flutes alone co-operate and endow the movement with tender, sorrowful charm. The following Alto aria obtains its mood through the captivating tones of the obligato Oboe d'amore. The Bass aria *Quoniam tu solus sanctus* is accompanied by a peculiar instrumental combination. The Corno da caccia, or Cor Anglais, with two Bassoons are added to the Continuo. The movement is difficult to realise and fails to come out clearly. This obstacle may be overcome by employing the Cembalo in place of the organ, but whether Bach used the Piano together with Organ in his religious works has never yet been ascertained. Critics of today are inclined to say not. The end of the *Gloria,* the *Cum sancto spiritu* is a masterpiece of brilliant writing. Note the wealth of thematic material in all its variety of form! From the very start each sound-group gives out its particular theme, which, in the course of the movement are combined and related in manifold ways. Remarkable, too, is the high range of the first Trumpet, (up to $\overline{\overline{d}}$ as early as the 4th bar), rendering this movement one of the most trying for the player. Indeed, the demands which Bach makes on the trumpeter far exceed those made by Händel, and can be fulfilled today by the best players only.

The third section of the Mass, the *Credo,* is, like the *Gloria* divided into separate sections. The opening movement was founded by Bach on a theme taken from a primitive Gregorian tune, which intones the Credo. Deep symbolism lies in the employment of this ancient mode. The whole movement grows out of it, as though from the very roots of faith; it never disappears for a moment; always recurs in the parts; ever manifesting itself, until, finally it is lost, as if in the broad stream of infinity. On one more occasion in this Mass does Bach make use of a Gregorian melody, that is in the number *Confiteor unum baptisma*. After it has been announced in bar 73 of this piece by the bass and alto, it is relegated to the tenor from the 92nd bar onwards in a broad "Cantus firmus". The symbolism is similar to that mentioned above:—The Holy Ghost, the third of the Godhead, manifested by Baptism. Equally symbolic is the treatment of the *Et in unum Dominum*, in the 3rd section of the *Credo*, (Duet) in strict Canon form. As both voices have but one single theme, yet at the same time two, so is the Son one with the Father, though both separate. Out of the wealth of beauty contained in this section I would point out but one detail:—The mysterious *Et incarnatus* with its peculiar continuous figure in the violins. "The heavenly spirit hovers anxiously over the world, seeking for one into whose soul it may enter." (Schweitzer.) The sorrowful *Crucifixus* is founded on a chromatic *Basso ostinato,* a repeated figure in the bass, four bars long. As

in the *Qui tollis* of the *Gloria* only the flutes are employed among the wood-wind instruments, and for the same reasons. The following "Et resurrexit" is of extraordinary magnificence, and a stronger contrast to the foregoing cannot be imagined. Trumpets and Drums supply the colour. At the passage *Cujus regnum non erit finis* one feels as though infinity were revealed to us. This magnificence is continued in the final Chorus *Et expecto resurrectionem* and it is to be noted how wonderfully Bach has prepared this section by the more simple sounding *Confiteor*.

And higher and ever higher surge the waves of this ocean of sound. The means of expression are enriched at every turn. In the *Sanctus,* which opens the 4th section of the Mass, a sixth part is added to the five-part Chorus, i. e. a second Alto. The canvas is *fresco,* not painting in detail, and masses of sound are marshalled to meet each other. The majesty and divinity of God are depicted in musical sound. In the following *Pleni sunt Coeli,* with its wonderful onward movement, it seems as though the whole creation joined in shouts of adoration. "Up to now Bach wished to portray only Christian songs of praise, but here, all the children of God and even the morning stars glorify the Lord"[*]). And even yet Bach has not reached the end of his resources. The following *Hosanna* forms the climax. Here, instead of the ordinary Chorus we have an 8 part double Chorus accompanied by full Orchestra in music

[*]) See Spitta: Bach, II, page 541.

of the highest ecstasy. So fiercely does the love of God burn in the master's spirit, that all earthly things are consumed. And he sees the heavens open and the Lord of Hosts sitting on a golden throne, surrounded by the Seraphim, who cry to each other, in double chorus, "Holy, holy, holy is God the Lord," with such voices that the pillars of the heavenly temple are shaken.*)

The following *Benedictus,* a Tenor Aria accompanied entirely by Solo Violin and Continuo returns to absolute simplicity. Quiet adoration replaces the former grandeur and brilliance. Equally simple is the *Agnus Dei,* an Alto Aria of unfathomable depth of feeling. But the *Dona nobis pacem* forms the conclusion to this gigantic work. It is founded on the *Gratias agimus* as a prayer of thanksgiving.

Bach's world of sound in the B minor Mass is never-ending and immeasurable. His works are a Book of Wisdom, the wisdom contained in the words of our Lord:—"Seek me, and ye shall surely find me."

Fritz Volbach.

---

*) See Spitta: Bach, II, page 541.

JOHANN SEBASTIAN BACH

MASS IN BMINOR

I. Kyrie

Soprano
+ Tenor

E. E. 3999

III. Credo

Et resurrexit tertia die secundum scripturas, et ascendit in coelum, sedet ad dexteram patris, et iterum venturus est cum gloria judicare vivos et mortuos, cujus regni non erit finis.

Et in spiritum sanctum, dominum et vivificantem, qui ex patre filioque procedit, qui cum patre et filio simul adoratur et conglorificatur, qui locutus est per prophetas. Et unam sanctum catholicam et apostolicam ecclesiam.

Confiteor unum baptisma in remissionem peccatorum, et expecto resurrectionem mortuorum et vitam venturi saeculi. Amen.

IV. Sanctus

Sanctus, sanctus, sanctus, dominus Deus Sabaoth! pleni sunt coeli et terra gloria ejus.

Osanna in excelsis.

Benedictus qui venit in nomine domini.

V. Agnus Dei

Agnus Dei, qui tollis peccata mundi, miserere nobis.

Dona nobis pacem.

VIII

JOHANN SEB. BACH, HOHE MESSE IN H MOLL

Wie riesiger Fels aus Urgestein getürmt, so ragt J. S. Bachs „Hohe Messe" empor. Hoch über den Wolken thront sein Gipfel in blauer Unendlichkeit, sonnenbestrahlt; in erhabener Einsamkeit, wohin kein anderer Klang zu dringen vermag. J. S. Bachs Kunst ist eine Kunst der Sehnsucht nach dem Ewigen. In der Liebe, — der Gottesminne — findet sie das Mittel, sich ihm zu nähern, der Liebe, die das Zeitliche in dem Ewigen, das Endliche in dem Unendlichen verschlingt. Eine Sehnsucht nach dem Unbekannten, Geheimnisvollen, zu Offenbarenden, eine Sehnsucht, die nur „durch Sehnen wird gestillt". —

Genaue Angaben über die Entstehung des Werkes lassen sich nicht machen. Die beiden ersten Teile der Messe, das Kyrie und Gloria, fügte Bach einem Gesuch an den König von Sachsen um Verleihung des Titels eines Hofkompositeurs bei, welches das Datum des 27. Juli 1733 trägt. Die Komposition der übrigen Teile — Credo, Sanctus und Osanna setzt Spitta in die Zeit von 1734—1738. Das Agnus Dei geht zurück auf eine Arie der Kantate „Lobet Gott in seinen Reichen" und das Dona nobis pacem ist in der Musik eine Wiederholung des Gratias agimus, das ebenfalls aus einer Kantate — Wir danken dir — stammt*).

Daß der Protestant Bach Messen komponiert, braucht uns nicht zu befremden. Luther hatte ja die Messe nicht abge-schafft, sondern ihr nur durch Ausscheidung des Opferakts den Charakter als Opfer genommen; die feststehenden Teile — das Ordinarium missae — bleiben auch im evangelischen Kultus bestehen. So sehen wir denn auch nach der Reformation bis in die Zeit Bachs eine Reihe evangelischer Meister Messen für den gottesdienstlichenGebrauch komponieren. Die wundervolle Dichtung, die alle Höhen und Tiefen religiösen Gefühls durchwandert, die Bilder aneinanderreiht, wie sie ergreifender und rührender, gewaltiger und majestätischer in abwechslungsvoller, sich steigernder Reihe nirgends herrlicher auftreten, bleibt ihnen erhalten. Wer aber war mehr berufen, die Herrlichkeit des hier geschilderten Gottesreiches in aller seiner Größe und Tiefe zu schildern, das geheimnisvolle, weit hinter aller Realität liegende Land des Sehnens zu durchwandern, als der größte deutsche Mystiker, als J. S. Bach? —

Aus tiefster Sehnsucht ist der erste Teil geboren, das Kyrie eleison; Sehnsucht nach Befreiung, nach Erlösung aus dieser Welt der Not, Verlangen, aufzugehen in der Liebe Gottes. Das ganze ergreifende Bild ist dargestellt in der Form einer fünfstimmigen Fuge. Die Besetzung des Chores: 2 Soprane, Alt, Tenor und Baß. Das Orchester besitzt neben dem Streichquintett an Bläsern 2 Flöten, 2 Oboe d'amore (d. s. Oboen, die eine Terz tiefer stehen als die gewöhnliche Oboe und im

---

*) Über die Beziehungen des Qui tollis zur Kantate „Schauet doch und sehet", des Patrem omnipotentem zu „Gott wie ist dein Name", des Crucifixus zu „Weinen, Klagen", des Osanna zu „Preise dein Glücke", s. A. Schweitzer: J. S. Bach (1908) S. 684 ff.

Klange weicher sind) und Fagotte. Die tiefste Stimme, der Continuo, wird außer von den Violoncelli und Kontrabässen auch von der Orgel gespielt. Letztere fügt zugleich die, durch die Generalbaßziffern vorgeschriebene Harmonie hinzu*). Das gilt nicht nur von diesem Satze, sondern von allen Sätzen des Werkes. Trotz der gewaltigen Dimensionen dieses Kyrie ist seine Gliederung eine klare und übersichtliche. 5 mächtige Einleitungstakte, dann Entwickelung des Fugenthemas im Orchester; hierauf übernimmt es der Chor in weit ausladender, breiter Darlegung. Aber der Inhalt ist noch nicht erschöpft, eine zweite gesteigerte Durchführung schließt sich an, durch ein Orchesterzwischenspiel in derselben Weise wie der erste Teil eingeleitet.

Das folgende Christe eleison ist als Duett behandelt. Die harmonische Füllung fällt hier der Orgel allein zu. Hoffnung und sichere Zuversicht bildet seine Grundstimmung. Diese Stimmung bleibt auch in dem anschließenden zweiten Kyrie, einem Stücke von wunderbarer Reinheit und Schönheit der Stimmführung. Die Instrumente gehen hier, mit Ausnahme des gewaltigen Fundaments, mit den Singstimmen. Man beachte die wunderbare Schlußsteigerung der letzten 9 Takte mit ihrer reichen Modulation.

Der 2. Teil des Werkes, das Gloria in excelsis Deo, ist nicht, wie es bei den früheren Meistern — nach kirchlicher Vorschrift — Gebrauch war (und wie es auch Beethoven tut), durchkomponiert, sondern in einzelne Teile zerlegt, von denen die drei ersten sich wieder zu einer einheitlichen Gruppe zusammenfassen lassen. Ein mächtiges Eingangstor bildet der erste Chor. Schmetternde, jubelnde Trompeten verleihen ihm hellen Glanz. Seine Zweiteilung ergibt sich aus dem Texte. In dem Laudamus wetteifern eine Solostimme und Sologeige in jubelndem Lobe des Herrn. Das Gratias agimus gründet sich auf zwei Themen, das Hauptthema gleich zu Beginn und das mit ihm herrlich verschlungene Nebenthema zu den Worten propter magnam gloriam tuam. — Mit dem folgenden Domine Deus beginnt eine Lobpreisung Christi. Wieder wechseln Solostücke mit Chören ab. Besonders hebe ich hervor das ergreifende Qui tollis. Von den Bläsern wirken hier nur die Flöten mit und verleihen dem Stücke seinen zarten, wehmütigen Reiz. Die folgende Alt-Arie Qui sedes charakterisiert ihre Stimmung durch den bestrickenden Klang der obligaten Oboe d'amore; vielleicht die schönste Stimme, die überhaupt für dieses Instrument geschrieben wurde. Eine ganz eigenartige instrumentale Zusammenstellung zeigt die Baß-Arie Quoniam tu solus sanctus. Zum Continuo treten Corno da caccia (Englisch Horn) und 2 Fagotte. Das Stück ist schwer zum Klingen zu bringen, es wirkt meist unklar. Mittels des Cembalo an Stelle der Orgel ist es möglich, diesen Übelstand zu heben. Ob aber Bach das Klavier in seinen kirchlichen Werken neben der Orgel angewandt hat, ist bis heute nicht sicher

---

*) Näheres über den Continuo und seine Behandlung siehe in der Einleitung zu Händels Messias.

X

entschieden. Unsere Zeit neigt mehr dazu, diese Frage zu verneinen. Der Schluß des Gloria, das Cum sancto spiritu ist ein Prachtstück rauschenden Glanzes. Man achte besonders auf den Reichtum der Thematik und die Verschiedenheit der Gestaltung der Themen. Gleich zu Anfang bringt jede Klanggruppe ihre eigenen Motive, die dann im Laufe der Durchführung des Satzes in eine reichere Beziehung und Wechselwirkung treten. Charakteristisch ist auch die hohe Führung der ersten Trompete (gleich im 4. Takt bis zum ä), die besonders diesen Satz zu einem der schwierigsten für den Bläser macht. Die Anforderungen, die Bach an den Trompeter stellt, gehen weit über die Händels hinaus und werden heute nur von den besten Spielern erfüllt.

Der 3. Teil, das Credo, ist wie das Gloria in eine Reihe einzelner Stücke zerlegt. Den einleitenden Satz, das Credo in unum Deum, baut Bach auf einem uralten, dem Gregorianischen Gesange entnommenen Thema auf, der Intonation des Credo. Eine tiefe Symbolik liegt in der Verwendung dieses Urmotivs. Aus ihm wächst, wie aus der Wurzel des Glaubens, der ganze Satz heraus; keinen Augenblick verschwindet es, immerfort klingt es weiter durch die Stimmen, sich aus sich selbst gebärend, wie die Gottheit, bis es schließlich in mächtiger Verbreiterung wie im breiten Strom der Ewigkeit sich verliert. Noch einmal verwendet Bach in diesem Werke eine gregorianische Melodie, und zwar in dem Satze Confiteor unum baptisma. Nachdem diese im 73. Takt dieses

Stückes in Baß und Alt sich ankündigt, bringt es der Tenor vom 92. Takt an als breiten Cantus firmus. Eine ähnliche Symbolik wie die oben genannte: Der hl. Geist, die dritte Person der Gottheit, der sich in der Taufe manifestiert. Symbolisch ist auch die Behandlung des Et in unum Dominum, des 3. Teiles des Credo (Duett) in streng kanonischer Führung. Beide Stimmen aus einem Thema und doch zwei, so ist auch der Sohn mit dem Vater eins und doch beide getrennt. Aus der Fülle unendlicher Schönheit dieses Teiles hebe ich nur Einzelnes hervor: das geheimnisvolle Et incarnatus mit der eigenartigen, fortlaufenden Geigenfigur. „Der himmlische Geist schwebt suchend über der Welt und sehnt sich nach einem Wesen, in das er eingehen könne." (Schweitzer.) Das sich anschließende, schmerzdurchzuckte Cruzifixus baut sich auf einem chromatischen Basso ostinato auf, einer immerfort wiederholten Figur der Bässe von 4 Takten. Auch hier von den Bläsern nur Flöten aus demselben Grunde, wie in dem Qui tollis des Gloria. Von erschütternder Pracht ist das folgende Et resurrexit, ein Gegensatz zu dem Vorigen, wie er gewaltiger nicht gedacht werden kann. Trompeten und Pauken geben das Kolorit. Bei der Stelle Cujus regnum non erit finis ist es, als ob die Unendlichkeit sich öffne. Dieser strahlende Glanz setzt sich fort in dem Schlußchor Et expecto resurrectionem. Man beachte, wie wunderbar Bach diesen Satz vorbereitet durch das klanglich schlichte Confiteor.

Und immer höher steigen die Wogen dieses tönenden Ozeans. Immer reicher werden die Mittel des Ausdrucks. Im Sanctus, das den 4. Teil der Messe eröffnet, tritt zu den 5 Stimmen des Chores noch eine 6., ein 2. Alt hinzu. An Stelle der Detailmalerei das al fresco. Massen bewegen sich gegeneinander. Majestät und die Erhabenheit Gottes klingen aus diesen Tönen. In dem folgenden Pleni sunt coeli, das in seiner steigenden Bewegung eine wunderherrliche Steigerung bedeutet, ist es, als ob die ganze Schöpfung mit einstimme in den Jubel. „Bisher wollte Bach nur Preis- und Wonnegesänge der Christenheit laut werden lassen, aber hier loben den Herrn die Morgensterne miteinander und jauchzen alle Kinder Gottes"*). Und noch immer nicht ist Bach am Ende der Steigerung. Den Höhepunkt bildet das folgende Osanna. Hier tritt an Stelle des einfachen der 8-stimmige Doppelchor, begleitet von allen Instrumenten. Eine Musik der höchsten Ekstase. So mächtig brennt die Gottesliebe im Herzen des Meisters, daß sie alles Irdische in ihm verzehrt. Und er sieht den Himmel offen und den Herrn Zebaoth auf goldenem Throne sitzen, umstanden von den Seraphim, die sich gegenseitig (Doppelchor) das „Heilig, heilig, heilig ist Gott der Herr" zurufen, mit solcher Stimme, daß die Schwellen des himmlischen Tempels erbeben**). — Das folgende Benedictus, eine Tenor-Arie, kehrt zu höchster Einfachheit zurück, Sologeige und Continuo bilden die ganze Begleitung. An Stelle des Glanzes und der Herrlichkeit ist nun die stille Anbetung getreten. Ebenso einfach ist das Agnus Dei, eine Alt-Arie von unergründlicher Tiefe des Gemüts. Den Abschluß des Riesenwerkes aber bildet das Dona nobis pacem auf die Musik des Gratias agimus. Durch diese Beziehung als Dankgebet charakterisiert.

Unerschöpflich und unermeßlich ist die Tonfülle J. S. Bachs, wie sie sich vor allem in seiner Hohen Messe offenbart; unerschöpflich an Reichtum, wie das Weltall. Ein Buch der Weisheit sind seine Werke, einer Weisheit, von der das Wort des Herrn gilt: „So ihr mich von Herzen suchet, so will ich mich finden lassen."

Fritz Volbach.

---

*) Siehe Spitta: Bach, II. S. 541. **) Vgl. ebenda.

Die HOHE MESSE in H moll

von

JOHANN SEBASTIAN BACH

E. E. 3999.

III. Credo

B. E. 3999.

DIE HOHE MESSE

I. KYRIE

№1

Adagio

Johann Sebastian Bach
1685 - 1750

Ernst Eulenburg Ltd.,
London · Zürich

No. 959

E.E. 3999

2

Largo ed un poco piano

E.E. 3999

4

5

E.E. 3999

6

8

11

E.E. 3999

12

E. E. 3999

14

E.E. 3999

15

E.E. 3999

18

E.E. 3999

22

E.E. 3999

23

E.E. 3999

24

E.E. 3999

26

E.E. 3999

28

E.E. 3999

30

E.E. 3999

32

S.I: le - - - i-son, Ky-ri-e e - - le - - - i-son, e - le - i - son.

S.II: - -i-son, e-le-i - son, Ky-ri-e e - - le - - - i-son, e - le - i - son.

A.: le - - i - son, Ky-ri-e e - le - - - - - i - son.

T.: - -i-son, Ky-ri - e - le-i-son, e - le - - - - i - son.

B.: - -i-son, e-le - - - - i-son, e - le - - - i - son.

E. E. 3999

34

38

E.E.3999

Nº 3

41

E. E. 3999

42

44

E.E.3999

45

E.E.3999

48

II. GLORIA.

N.° 4

49

E.E.3999

50

E.E.3999

51

E.E.3999

52

E.E.3999

58

E.E.3999

62

E.E.3999

64

E.E.3999

68

E.E.3999

E.E.8999

E.E.3999

E. E. 3999

74

S.I: ta-tis, pax,pax, pax, pax, in ter - ra pax ___ ho - mi -

A.: - nae vo-lun-ta - - tis, in ter - ra pax ___ homi-nibus bo-nae

T.: ta - - - - - - - - - - - - - tis, bo - nae

B.: ___ in - ter - ra pax ho-mi-nibus bonae volun - ta - - tis, bo - nae

E.E.3999

E.E.3999

E.E.3999

80

E.E.3999

Nº 5. Aria.

82

E.E.3999

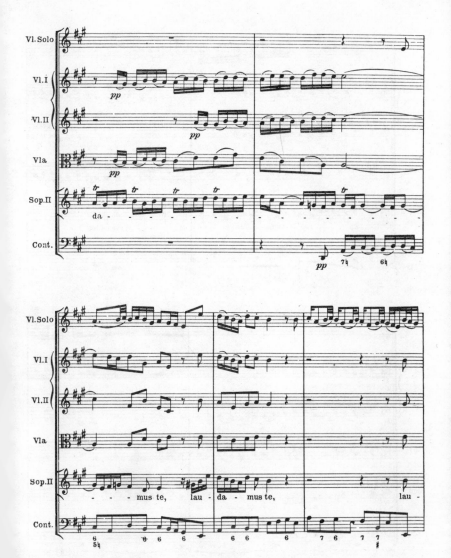

E.E.3999

84

E.E.3999

E.E.3999

88

E.E.3999

89

E.E.3999

92

E. E. 3999

94

Nº 6.

E.E.3999

95

E.E.3999

E.E. 3999

98

Vocal text:

- S.I II: am, pro-pter ma - gnam glo - - - riam tu - am.
- A.: a - gimus ti - bi pro - pter ma - gnam glo - riam tu - am.
- T.: - ti-as a - gimus ti-bi propter ma - gnam glo - riam tu - am.
- B.: - am, pro-pter magnam glo - riam tu - am.

E. E. 3999

№ 7. DUETTO.

104

E.E. 3999

105

E.E. 3999

108

E.E. 3999

110

112

E.E.3999

114

E. E. 3999

No 8.
Lento.

Flauto traverso I

Flauto traverso II

Violino I — senza sordino

Violino II — senza sordino

Viola — senza sordino

Soprano II

Alto — Qui tol-lis pec - ca - - - - ta mun - di,

Tenore — Qui tol-lis pec - ca - - - ta

Basso

Violoncello — coll' arco e staccato

Continuo

Fl.tr. I
Fl.tr. II

Vl.I

Vl.II

Vla

S.II — Qui tol - lis pec - ca - - -

A. — mi-se-re-re no-bis, mi - se - re - - -

T. — mun - - di, mi-se-re-re no - bis, mi - se -

B. — Qui tol - lis pec -

Vcl.

Cont.

122

E.E.8999

Nº 9. ARIA.

124

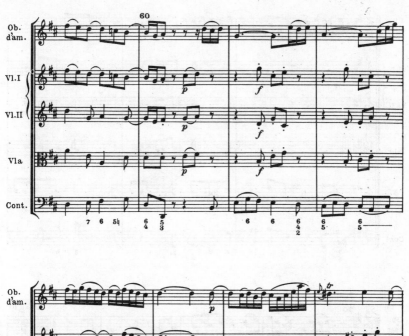

Ob. d'am.

Vl. I

Vl. II

Vla

A. -se - re - re no - bis, qui se - - -

Cont.

Adagio

Ob. d'am.

Vl. I
pp

Vl. II
pp

Vla
pp

A. - - - des ad dextram Patris, mi - se - re - re

Cont.

132

Pa - - tris, mi - - se - re - re no - bis!

№ 10. ARIA

134

E. E. 3999

136

E.E. 3999

138

E.E. 3999

140

E.E. 3999

142

lus al - tis — si - mus Je - su Chri - ste.

N.º 11

Vivace.

145

E. E. 3999

146

E. E. 3999

148

E. E. 3999

149

E.E. 3999

151

E.E.3999

154

E.E.3999

155

E.E.3999

E.E.3999

160

E.E.3999

162

E.E.3999

164

E.E.3999

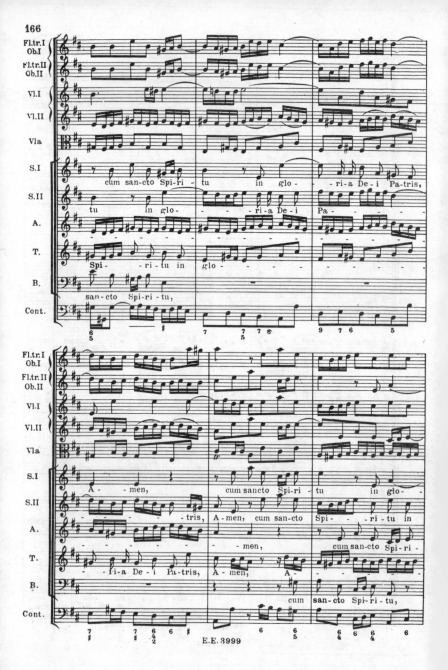

E.E.3999

168

E.E.3999

170

110

E.E.3999

172

E.E.3999

E.E.3999

III. CREDO.

179

E. E. 3999

E. E. 3999

N.° 13

184

E.E. 3999

185

E. E. 3999

186

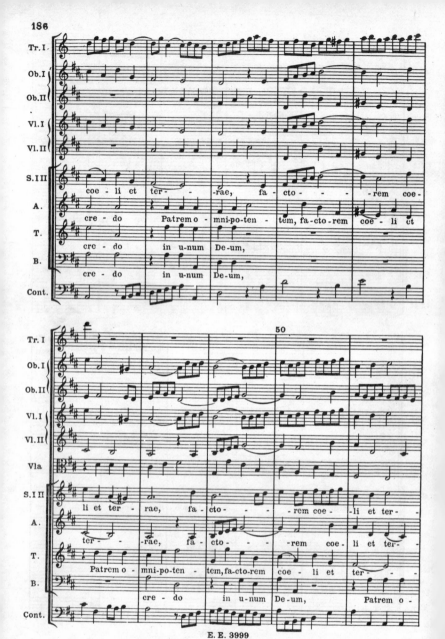

E. E. 3999

187

E. E. 3999

188

E. E. 3999

189

E. E. 3999

E.E. 3999

№ 14. DUETTO

Andante

193

E.E.3999

194

E.E.3999

198

E.E.3999

200

E.E.3999

202

E.E.3999

E. E.3999

204

et qui propter nostram sa-lu - - tem de-scen - - - dit de coe-lis.

propter nostram sa-lu - - tem de-scen-dit de coe - - lis.

E.E.3999

E.E.3999

206

E. E. 3999

208

E. E. 3999

Nº 16

210

E.E.3999

E.E.3999

214

Nº 17

E.E.3999

216

E.E.3999

217

E.E.3999

218

E.E.3999

219

E.E.3999

E.E.3999

222

E. E. 3999

226

E. E. 3999

229

E. E. 3999

230

70

et i - te -

E. E. 3999

234

E. E. 3999

235

E. E. 3999

E. E. 3999

288

110

E. E. 3999

240

Nº 18. ARIA

244

E. E. 3999

248

E.E. 3999

E. E. 3999

252

E. E. 3999

254

S.I fi - te - or u - num ba -ptisma in re -mis - si - o - - - nem

S.II or u - -num ba - pti - sma in re - missi - o - nem pecca -

A. to - - rum, in re - missi - o - - - nem pec - ca -

T. - te - or u - num ba -ptisma in re - missi o - - nem pecca - to rum,

B. or u -num ba -ptisma in re - missi - o - - nem pecca - to - - - -

Cont.

70

S.I pecca - to - - - rum, in re - missi - o - - nem pecca - to - -

S.II torum, pecca - to - - rum, in re - missi - o - - nem pec-ca - to -

A. torum, pecca - to - - rum, in re - missi - o - - nem pec - - ca - to-

T. pec - ca - to - - - rum, in re - missi - o -nem pecca - to - - -

B. - - - - - rum,

Cont.

E. E. 3999

255

E. E. 3999

258

Adagio.

E. E. 3999

260

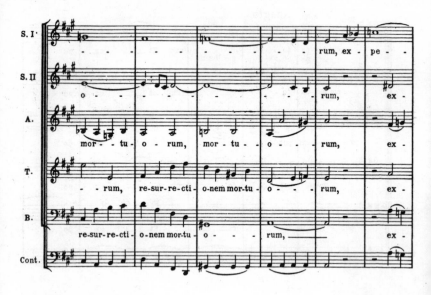

E. E. 3999

Vivace e Allegro.

266

E. E. 3999

268

o-nem mor-tu - o - - - rum,   re-sur - re-cti - o - -

o-nem mor-tu - o - - - rum,

o - nem,   re-sur - re-cti-o - - - - - nem

o-nem mor-tu - o - - - rum,

— nem mor-tu - o - - - rum,

E.E. 3999

270

E.E. 3999

274

275

E. E. 3999

278

E. E. 3999

IV. Sanctus

№ 20.

281

E. E. 3999

282

234

E. E. 3999

285

E. E. 3999

286

E. E. 3999

294

298

E. E. 3999

E. E. 3999

300

E. E. 3999

302

303

E. E. 3999

304

E.E. 3999

305

306

E. E. 3999

309

312

E.E. 3999

Nº 21

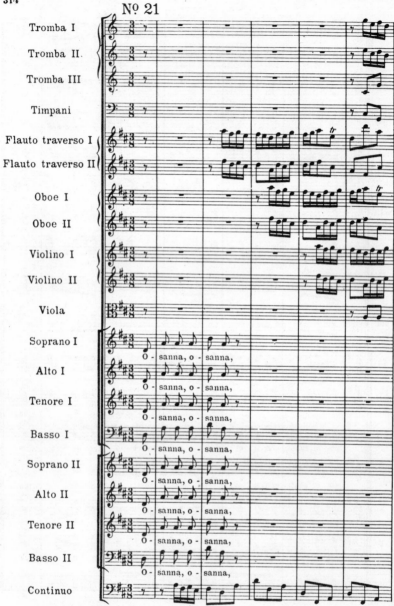

E. E. 3999

316

S.I: o - sanna in ex - cel-sis, o - san -
A.I: o - sanna in ex - cel-sis, o - san -
T.I: o - sanna in ex - cel-sis,
B.I: o - sanna in ex - cel-sis,

S.II: san-na, o - sanna in ex - cel-sis,
A.II: san-na, o - sanna in ex - cel-sis,
T.II: san-na, o - sanna in ex - cel-sis,
B.II: san-na, o - sanna in ex - cel-sis,

E. E. 3999

317

E. E. 8999

318

E. E. 3999

320

E. E. 3999

325

E. E. 3999

326

E. E. 3999

330

E. E. 3999

331

E.E. 3999

832

E.E. 3999

333

E. E. 3999

336

E.E.3999

338

№ 22. ARIA.

Be - ne - dictus, be - - - ne - dictus qui ve - nit, qui

Osanna da Capo.

p. 314

V. AGNUS DEI.

E.E. 3999

344

Nº 24.

346

E. E. 3999

E. E. 3999

350

E. E.3999

352

E.E.3999

Fine.